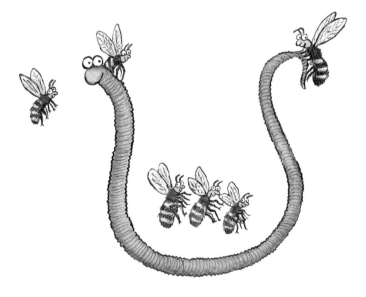

Published in the UK by Alison Green Books, 2023
An imprint of Scholastic
1 London Bridge, London, SE1 9BG
Scholastic Ireland, 89E Lagan Road, Dublin Industrial Estate, Glasnevin, Dublin, D11 HP5F

SCHOLASTIC and associated logos are trademarks and/or
registered trademarks of Scholastic Inc.

Text © Julia Donaldson, 2010, 2012, 2014, 2016, 2019, 2023
Illustrations © Axel Scheffler, 2010, 2012, 2014, 2016, 2019, 2023
Activities created by Little Wild Things © Julia Donaldson, 2023
Based on the bestselling picture books *The Smeds and the Smoos*, *Superworm*,
The Scarecrows' Wedding, *Zog* and *Zog and the Flying Doctors*

The right of Julia Donaldson and Axel Scheffler to be identified
as the author and illustrator of this work has been asserted by them under the Copyright, Designs
and Patents Act 1988.

ISBN 978 07023 1930 3

A CIP catalogue record for this book is available from the British Library.

Printed in China.
Paper made from wood grown in sustainable forests and other controlled sources.

1 3 5 7 9 10 8 6 4 2

This is a work of fiction. Names, characters, places, incidents and dialogues are products of the
author's imagination or are used fictitiously. Any resemblance to actual people, living or dead, events
or locales is entirely coincidental.

www.scholastic.co.uk

MIX
Paper | Supporting
responsible forestry
FSC® C008047

SUPERWORM
AND FRIENDS

Outdoor Activity Book

Based on the picture books by Julia Donaldson
and Axel Scheffler
Activities created by Little Wild Things

ALISON
GREEN
BOOKS

CONTENTS

SUPERWORM

THE SCARECROWS' WEDDING

CONTENTS

ZOG

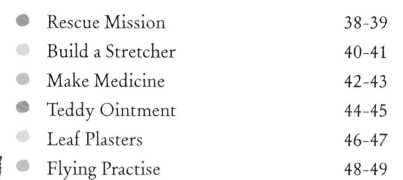

THE SMEDS AND THE SMOOS

Letter from Little Wild Things

Dear adventurers,

Welcome to your very own outdoor activity book!

We are Little Wild Things, a small community organisation whose mission is to get children playing outdoors. We love helping children explore the natural world and giving them new ideas for games and adventures to try outside.

We think spending time outside is really important and so want to make outdoor play as fun and easy as possible. This book is bursting with ideas inspired by four of our favourite picture books by Julia Donaldson and Axel Scheffler. Use them for a party, in the school holidays, when you're out for a walk, in the sunshine and in the rain!

Get outside and go wild!

Little Wild Things

Hints and Tips

* Ask a grown-up to read through the instructions with you and set up any bits and pieces you need help with.

* Don't worry if you don't have much outside space – plenty of these activities can be done anywhere. Make your way to a park, your nearest playground, or even just the street outside.

* Sometimes you'll want to collect things or dig in the ground. Check with your grown-up that you're allowed to before you start!

* Remember to always collect things from the ground rather than picking living flowers or branches.

* Outdoor play can be a little messy so make sure you don't wear your smartest clothes, and always give your hands a good wash after you're finished!

Let's get playing!

SUPERWORM

Superworm is super-long.
Superworm is super-strong.
Watch him wiggle! See him squirm!
Hip, hip, hooray for SUPERWORM!

Superworm is always having fun outdoors, whether
he's saving his friends from busy roads, or escaping
from wicked Wizard Lizard's magic flower.

Step outside and see what adventures you can have
with these Superworm-inspired activities.

SEARCH FOR SUPERWORM

Follow these simple steps to charm worms from the soil. Perhaps you'll even find Superworm!

ADVENTURE KIT

* A small trowel or spade

* A bucket or other container

WHAT TO DO

1. Find a soft bit of ground or an empty flowerbed that you are allowed to dig in.

2. Now stamp on your patch of ground with both feet, bang it with your spade and even try jumping up and down on it. Keep this up for at least 30 seconds.

3. Next, use your spade to carefully turn over some of the soil and crumble lumps gently in your fingers.

4. You should find some worms who have come to the surface. Pop any worms you find into your bucket. Put some soil or old leaves in with them and keep the bucket out of the sun. Keep stamping and digging until you have a good collection of worms.

5. Now it's time to look closely at your worms. Look to see which end is at the front when your worm moves forwards. The front end will be the head!

HINTS AND TIPS

Remember to be kind and gentle with your worms. Always try and dig around worms and lift them out in a piece of soil rather than pulling them straight out of the ground – you don't want to stretch them!

KEEP ADVENTURING

You can often see birds doing a spot of worm charming: drumming their feet on a patch of ground to bring some worms to the surface for a tasty supper. Keep a look out when you're next in the park.

6. Can you measure your worms? You could carefully put a few side by side to see which is the longest and which is the fattest.

7. Once you've finished collecting and investigating your worms, put them back where you found them.

So how does worm charming work?

Worms have bristles all over their bodies which can sense movements in the soil. When we stamp on the ground, worms feel the soil shaking and start moving upward towards the surface to try and escape from any hungry creatures that may be about. Then it's easier for us to dig them up! Though luckily for them we aren't planning to eat them for dinner…

MUDDY MEALS

Superworm will need to keep his strength up if he's going to keep on saving the day. Can you make him something delicious for lunch?

WHAT TO DO

1. Find a place with lots of mud that you are allowed to dig in and make messy.

2. Use your spoon to pop some mud into one of your containers. Add a small amount of water and give the mud a stir with your mixing stick.

3. Once you have a good supply of lovely gooey mud, it's time to start creating! First, take a leaf and dollop a spoonful of mud into the middle. Use the spoon to spread the mud out carefully to cover the whole leaf, right to the edges. Then press another leaf down on top and you have a mud sandwich!

ADVENTURE KIT

* Some containers that can get dirty

* A spoon

* A mixing stick

* Some water

* Leaves, petals, grass, sticks and stones

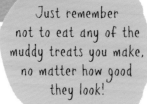

Just remember not to eat any of the muddy treats you make, no matter how good they look!

HINTS AND TIPS

Worms eat almost anything that has fallen down into the soil. Therefore feel free to spice up your mud mixtures with any natural things you find in your garden or mud patch. Your worm customers will love the variety!

6. Mud sandwiches, mud soup and mud cakes are all big hits with worms, but once you've got a good mud mixture to work with, you can make anything you fancy! Why not try creating a massive mud pie, a mud sausage or even a mud lollipop! Once you've finished mixing and making, don't forget to display all your creations on a selection of leaves and stones. Delicious!

4. Next, mix some mud with a few stones, leaves and bits of grass until you have a nice chunky mixture. Grab a handful and roll it between your palms until you have a small round ball. Press the ball gently on to a big leaf or stone and decorate it with any petals and small sticks you have. You've made a muddy cupcake!

5. Finally, try adding a few spoonfuls of mud, some more water and some ripped-up leaves to another container and stir it up to make some mud soup.

KEEP ADVENTURING

Why not make some labels for your muddy treats so your customers can see what you have on offer and decide what they might like to sample?

MUD PAINTING

Worms chew up old leaves and bits of wood to make lovely muddy soil. This is great for plants and trees but did you know you can also use mud in your artwork? Paint yourself a muddy masterpiece!

ADVENTURE KIT

* A bowl or container that can get dirty

* A spoon

* A mixing stick

* Some water

* Something to paint

* A paintbrush

WHAT TO DO

1. Gather the things you need and find a place with lots of mud that you are allowed to dig in and make messy.

2. Use your spoon to dig around in the mud and loosen it up a little. Use your fingers to pick out any stones and roots and then put four or five spoonfuls of the mud into your bowl.

3. Add a small amount of water and give the mud a stir with your mixing stick, using the bottom of the stick to break up any lumps.

4. Keep stirring and adding water a little at a time until your mud paint is smooth and runny.

5. Next, decide where you're going to paint. You could paint a tree, some leaves and stones, or even on the patio if you're allowed to.

6. Now experiment with your mud paint to see how it goes on. First try painting a big square or some long lines. You can always add more water if your paint is too thick or more mud if it's too runny.

HINTS AND TIPS

* Mud can be brown, yellow, red, grey or even black. Try finding mud from different places to see how many different paint colours you can mix up.

* If you don't have a paintbrush, you could use a leaf, a stick, a handful of moss, or even your fingers.

KEEP ADVENTURING

Once you've finished creating, you can enjoy cleaning off your painty masterpieces with a little water. Then your surfaces will be ready to paint all over again!

7. See if you can paint some patterns and shapes too. Muddy stars, stripes and dots will all look awesome. Can you try painting your name in mud? What about painting your hand or foot all over with your paint and making a muddy print. Mudtastic!

SUPERWORM LASSO

Help! Disaster! Baby toad
Has hopped on to a major road.
"Quick! Whatever can we do?"
Look — a SUPERWORM lasso!

Have fun acting out Superworm's heroic rescue
with some teddies and some string.

WHAT TO DO

1. Use two lines of sticks to create the outline of a road on the ground. Your pretend road could be long and straight, go around corners or turn in a big circle.

2. Once you're happy with your road, it's time to create your Superworm lasso. Take one of your animal teddies and ask your grown-up to carefully tie one end of your piece of rope or string around its body, leaving the other end of the rope nice and long. This is your Superworm lasso.

ADVENTURE KIT

* Some animal teddies

* A one metre long piece of string

* Lots of sticks

* Some toy cars, trucks or tractors

* A flat space to build a road outline

* Someone to play with

Make sure to only play on your pretend road and never near any real roads!

HINTS AND TIPS

* Soft teddies are best so they don't hurt if they bonk you on the nose when they're being lassoed to safety!
* If you don't have sticks for the edge of your road, why not use blocks, string or stones instead.

3. Now position your teddy in the middle of the road. Stand back from the road and hold the other end of the lasso in your hands.

4. Get a friend or grown-up to drive one of your toy cars down the road towards your teddy.

5. Hold tightly to the end of the rope and before the car gets too close, give the lasso a big tug so your teddy is pulled to safety. Phew! Superworm has saved the day!

6. Take it in turns to drive the cars and pull the Superworm lasso. How many animals will he rescue today?

KEEP ADVENTURING

Where else can you rescue your animal teddies from? Can your Superworm lasso also pull them away from a hungry crocodile or haul them out of a tree?

SUPER STRENGTH

Are you feeling as strong as Superworm today?
Why not test your strength with this fun game.

ADVENTURE KIT

* A piece of rope or string about 1.5
metres long — if you don't have a rope,
try an old dressing gown tie

* Some short logs or sticks of
different thicknesses

* An outdoor area with plenty of
flat space

WHAT TO DO

1. Take the piece of rope
and tie it around the centre
of one of your logs. Get a
grown-up to help with the
knot if you need to.

2. Tie a loop in the other
end of the rope to make
a handle.

3. Pull hard on the rope handle to make sure your knot stays in place.

4. Now set up a start and finish line. You can use sticks, stones, or a rucksack, or mark a line on the ground. Ready your super muscles and try dragging your log from the start to the finish as quickly as you can.

HINTS AND TIPS

If the string is hurting your hands, you could make it more comfortable by wrapping a tea towel round the handle.

KEEP ADVENTURING

Now you have the hang of log dragging why not see if you can set up an obstacle course with things to drag your log over and around. Can you time yourself and beat your record or find a friend to race against?

5. Once you've had a few tries, challenge yourself by tying your string onto a bigger log and dragging that!

6. Once your muscles are super warm, you can even see if you can drag two logs at once, or try dragging your log up a hill!

WIGGLY WORMS

Watch him wiggle! See him squirm!
Hip, hip, hooray for SUPERWORM!

Make some wiggly worms with this tissue paper trick!

ADVENTURE KIT

* A roll of toilet paper

* A pencil

* A small bowl of water

* A pipette or a teaspoon

WHAT TO DO

1. Separate the toilet tissue into square sheets by pulling carefully along the dotted lines between each square. You can make as many worms as the number of sheets you have!

2. Lay one square of toilet paper out on a flat surface and place the pencil on it diagonally with the middle of the pencil in one corner of the square.

KEEP ADVENTURING:

Can you make rainbow worms by using felt tip pens to dot some colour on your tissue paper before you roll it up? What happens if you use two pieces of paper to make your worm? Challenge your friends – who can make their worm grow and wiggle the most?

3. Wrap the corner of the tissue paper around the pencil and roll the pencil towards you. Once you have rolled the whole sheet around the pencil, give the free corner a little lick to stick it down.

HINTS AND TIPS

Be sure to make your worms on a dry surface, or they'll get damp as you make them and then they won't wiggle so well.

4. Stand the pencil up and use your other hand to press down on the tissue paper, squashing it down to the bottom of the pencil. Once it's squashed down all the way round, carefully wiggle it off the bottom of the pencil. This is your worm!

5. To make your worm wiggle, simply use your pipette or a teaspoon to carefully drip a few drops of water on to your worm's body. Now watch him wiggle, and see him squirm!

6. Once your worm is wet through, it won't wiggle or grow any more – so just pop it in the compost bin and make another one! You can keep making them until your tissue runs out.

The Scarecrows' Wedding

"Let's have a wedding, the best wedding yet,
A wedding that no one will ever forget."

Betty O'Barley and Harry O'Hay are two scarecrows planning their wedding. They need to collect all sorts of finery from around the farm, and they mustn't forget the pink flowers!

Can you help Betty and Harry celebrate by creating some fabulous feathery headdresses and some incredible leaf confetti?

FLOWER POWER

Harry O'Hay finds Betty some pink flowers for their wedding. Have fun making a colourful flower picture with leaves and petals. What colours will you choose?

ADVENTURE KIT

* An A4-sized piece of white or pale material

* Some leaves and petals of different shapes and sizes

* A smooth rock that fits in your hand

WHAT TO DO

1. First, lay out your piece of material somewhere nice and flat, then fold it in half along the long side, pressing down firmly on the fold. Unfold your piece of material carefully and you will be left with a crease down the middle.

2. Now choose a few leaves and petals and place them on just one half of your material. You could put them dotted all over, in a spiral pattern or even make a smiley face!

3. Keep placing the leaves and petals on one half of your material until you are happy with the pattern you have created.

4. Bring the empty half of the material up and over your pattern so that leaves and petals are trapped inside. Do this carefully so you don't upset your pattern.

5. Now it is time to start bashing! Take the stone in your hand, making sure your fingers are not tucked underneath, and bring it down firmly on top of the material. Be careful not to bash too hard otherwise the leaves and petals will start to jump around and mix up the pattern you created.

KEEP ADVENTURING

You could use your new skills to make colourful bunting, a new picture to go on your wall, or jazzy cards to send to all your friends.

6. Keep bashing your piece of material all over, always being careful not to hurt your fingers, until you can see some colour coming through. Be sure to bash every bit!

7. Now it is time to reveal your picture! Unfold the piece of material and pick off the bashed leaves and petals. Which made the best and most colourful marks? Where will you display your colourful creation?!

HINTS AND TIPS

* Really juicy leaves and petals work best for this.
* Choose a non-shiny material so the colours can soak through for the best results.
* If you don't have any material, this also works well with absorbent paper or card.

MAKE A FEATHER HEADBAND

The geese each lend Betty O'Barley a feather to make her dress. It might be tricky to collect enough feathers to make a whole dress like Betty's, but how about making one of these funky feather headbands?

Always ask an adult to help when using scissors

ADVENTURE KIT

* A long strip of material, about 10cm wide

* Safety scissors

* 3 or 4 feathers

* Double-sided tape

WHAT TO DO

1. Check your material strip is long enough to tie around your head. Place the middle of the strip against your forehead and then ask a grown-up to tie a knot in the material at the back of your head. If it is much too long, use your scissors to trim it down a bit.

2. Once you know the material fits, untie the knot and lay the strip out somewhere flat. If your material is coloured or patterned on one side only, lay the side you would like to see face down.

3. Now take your double-sided tape and stick a strip around 20 cm long in the middle and along the top edge of your material.

HINTS AND TIPS

* Long feathers with a good long quill at the bottom are best for this.
* Remember to make sure all the double-sided tape is covered with material, otherwise sticky bits can end up pulling on your hair!

6. Take the bottom half of your material strip and press it up on to the tape over the top of the feather quills. The tape will stick to the material and the feathers will be held in place. Make sure it is held nice and firmly. Now you are ready to deck yourself out in your feathery finery!

4. Carefully peel off the plastic backing and then grab your feathers.

5. Stick your feathers down one at a time by placing the quill at the bottom onto the strip of tape. The main fluffy part of the feather will then poke up and over the piece of material. You may want to put all your feathers in a bundle in the centre or space them out evenly along the tape, whichever you prefer.

KEEP ADVENTURING

Now you know how to make a headband why not try using some other natural materials to create lots of different styles. Lavender stalks, leaves and long grass can all look brilliant. Can you make headbands for your whole family?

MAKE A LEAF DECORATION

Betty and Harry use lots of lovely natural things to make their wedding special. See if you can make a beautiful leaf decoration to brighten up your room.

ADVENTURE KIT

* A piece of string around 30cm long

* A short stick

* A short pipe cleaner

* A place with lots of colourful fallen leaves

* Safety scissors

Always ask an adult to help when using scissors

WHAT TO DO

1. Prepare your piece of string. Tie one end of the string to the short stick and the other end to the middle of the pipe cleaner. Fold the pipe cleaner in half and twist the two halves together nice and tightly.

2. Now collect your leaves! Look for different colours, sizes and shapes to make your decoration really beautiful.

3. Next, hold the pipe cleaner with one hand and pick up a leaf up with the other.

4. Push the pipe cleaner though the middle of the leaf until the top half is poking through.

5. Now let go of the leaf and use this hand to take hold of the top of the pipe cleaner.

6. Then use your other hand to gently push the leaf all the way down to the stick at the bottom of the string.

HINTS AND TIPS

* Autumn is the best time of year to make these decorations when there are lots of lovely crisp leaves to find.
* Leaves sometimes tear when you are pushing them onto the string so try to add them gently. If any do break then just pull them off and pick another one – there will be plenty to choose from!

KEEP ADVENTURING

Why not turn your decoration into a caterpillar? Add some stickers for eyes, pipe cleaners for legs and draw a big smiley mouth with a felt tip pen.

7. Keep adding leaves in this way until your string is as full as you would like it, just make sure to leave a bit of space at the top of the string to make a loop for hanging.

8. Once you're done, ask a grown-up to cut off the pipe cleaner and tie the top part of the string into a loop so that you can hang your decoration up. Will it go on your bedroom wall or take centre stage at your teddies' next party?

LEAF CONFETTI

Make some leaf confetti to throw over
Harry and Betty, or anyone else
for that matter!

Always ask an adult to help when using a hole punch

ADVENTURE KIT

* A hole punch

* A small pot

* Somewhere to collect a few leaves

WHAT TO DO

1. First find some leaves to make your confetti. Stiff, waxy ones from an evergreen plant like ivy are best. Check with your grown-up before you choose your leaves. Collect five or six to start with.

2. Find a flat surface and grab your hole punch. Take a leaf and slide it into the slot where the holes are made. Ask a grown-up to help you with this for the first time if you're not sure where the leaf should go.

3. Press down firmly on the hole punch until you hear a click. This click is the hole being made in the leaf. Now pull the leaf out carefully and look at the hole.

7. You can try different leaves to make yourself a range of confetti with different colours and textures.

8. Now decide who you will be throwing it over. Will some of your teddies be getting married or will there be some other celebration? Could your favourite car be winning a race, or are all your toys having a party?

9. Once you're ready, take a pinch of leaf confetti in each hand, count to three and then fling your handfuls as high into the air as you can and watch them flutter down. Hooray!

4. Next, take a look under the hole punch and find the little round piece of leaf you've punched out. This is your leaf confetti.

5. Turn the leaf around and slide it back into the hole punch so you can make another hole. Keep turning your leaf and punching holes to make more leaf confetti.

6. Once you have a pile of confetti, pop it into your pot.

KEEP ADVENTURING

Instead of throwing your confetti, could you use it with some glue and card to make a cool picture or even a wedding invitation?

NATURAL PAINTS

Harry and Betty use all kinds of colourful things to make their wedding day special. Can you find some natural items around you to mix up lots of colourful paints?

ADVENTURE KIT

* Some water

* A pestle and mortar or an old saucepan and a rock

* Colourful things to crush up – leaves, petals, mud and moss all work well

* Old yogurt pots to put your paint into

* An old cloth or towel

* A paintbrush

*Something to paint on

WHAT TO DO

1. Gather the things you need from your garden or park. Try and collect a variety of colours so you can make a great mix of paints.

2. Arrange the things you have collected into piles according to colour.

3. Add some small pieces from one of your piles to the mortar bowl or saucepan. Pop in a few spoonfuls of water and then get crushing. Rub the pestle or the rock hard against the bottom of the mortar bowl or saucepan. The harder you rub, the more colourful your paint will be.

4. Slowly add a little more water to see what colour you've made.

5. Once you're happy with your paint, tip it out into one of your pots or bowls ready to use later.

6. Give your mortar bowl a wipe out with the old cloth and you are ready to try something else from one of your other piles and crush it up to make a new colour.

HINTS AND TIPS

* Dandelions make a great yellow paint — you may even have some growing in your garden!
* If you're trying this in the autumn blackberries are brilliant for making purple paint — just take care that you don't stain your clothes!

KEEP ADVENTURING

Why not try potato printing with your paints, painting your feet for colourful footprints or painting your patio if you don't have any paper at home! Can you make new colours by mixing some of your paints together? What happens when you mix all of your colours together?!

7. Keep crushing and mixing until you have a whole palette full of colour! Which of your natural items makes the best coloured paint?

8. Once you've finished mixing paints, see how creative you can be. You can use your paints to paint a picture on paper or card, or if you're out and about, see if you can paint on a rock, a log or a tree trunk.

SHINY SHELLS

Betty wears a necklace of pearly pink shells when she marries Harry. Can you clean and polish some shells to make them shiny enough for a wedding day?

ADVENTURE KIT

* Some sea shells or snail shells

* A bowl of soapy water

* An old toothbrush or nailbrush

* A paintbrush

* A small container of vegetable oil

* An old cloth

* Somewhere to display your collection

WHAT TO DO

1. First, lay out all the things you need. Now take your shells and pop them into the bowl of soapy water one at a time. Once they are wet, use the toothbrush or nailbrush to give them a really good scrub.

2. Give your shells a quick rub dry with the old cloth, then take the paintbrush and dip the end into the vegetable oil and carefully brush the top of one shell with a little oil.

3. Next grab the old cloth again and use it to really rub the oil into all the cracks and crevices.

4. Turn your shell over so that you can oil and polish the underneath in the same way.

5. Once all your shells are cleaned and polished take some time to look at them and see how beautiful they are. Can you see colours and sparkles you didn't notice in them before?

KEEP ADVENTURING

Why not try decorating a box to keep your shell collection in. An old egg or shoe box would work well. You could also add some tissue paper or an old bit of material to keep your shells safe.

6. Now find somewhere special to display your beautiful shiny shell collection! A rock, a log or on the shelf in your bedroom, you decide!

HINTS AND TIPS

* This works really well with rocks too. Rocks often look much more exciting when they are super clean and shiny!
* Remember that oil can stain your clothes so don't wear your best outfit while you're polishing, or cover up with an apron.

ZOG

Then Zog said, "Flying doctors! I'd love to join the crew.
If you'll let me be your ambulance, then I can carry you."

The Flying Doctors love to heal all sorts of injured animals
and people. Pearl and Gadabout use ointments, medicine and bandages to
help their friends, and Zog carries them through
the air as a flying ambulance.

Turn the page to become a member of their crew!

RESCUE MISSION

The Flying Doctors are always on the look-out for animals that need their help. Who will need *your* help today?

WHAT TO DO

1. Ask a grown-up to help you prepare your teddies for rescuing by hiding them far and wide. Some of them might be trapped under logs, others could be stuck under stones and some may even be dangling from trees!

2. Next, prepare yourself for the rescue. Decide on a safe place to bring any teddies you find. Then practise your best and loudest nee-naw sound.

Nee-Naw!

Nee-Naw!

ADVENTURE KIT

* Some teddies that need rescuing

* Lots of space to run around

* A grown-up to help set things up

3. There's not a moment to lose! As soon as you're ready, get searching, keeping your eyes open and your ears pricked for any cries for help. Remember to keep up your nee-naw sound so that the teddies know that help is on the way!

KEEP ADVENTURING

Once all your teddies have been rescued, decide what treatment they might need. Will they need medicine, some ointment or just a plaster? Take a look at the next few activities for some ideas!

Nee-Naw! Nee-Naw! Nee-Naw!

HINTS AND TIPS

Your teddies might get a bit grubby during a rescue mission, so make sure you play with ones that will enjoy a trip to the washing machine!

4. When you find a teddy, take a moment to think about things. Can you try to make the rescue on your own, or do you need a grown-up to help? You may need to lift some sticks and branches or reach up to rescue someone from a tree.

5. Once the teddy is free, reassure them that they are safe and all will be well.

6. Take your rescued teddy back to your safe place and lay them down gently. Then set off again to see who else needs your help!

BUILD A STRETCHER

The flying doctors use stretchers to carry their patients from place to place. Can you build a stretcher to carry your teddies?

ADVENTURE KIT

* A rectangle of material around 50cm long and 35cm wide – you could use an old tea towel

* Two straight sticks around 70cm long

* Double-sided tape

* Some animal teddies

WHAT TO DO

1. Lay out your material on a flat surface with one of the long edges facing you.

2. Put a stick on the material in line with the long edge, around 10cm in, leaving enough cloth to wrap around the stick.

3. Stick three or four short sections of double-sided tape along the very edge of the material.

4. Peel off the backing on the double-sided tape. Lift the edge of the material, bring it up and over the stick and press it firmly down on the material on the other side. The main part of the stick should be covered and held tightly by the material and the two ends of the stick will poke out of the material at either end and can be used as handles.

HINTS AND TIPS

* When two of you are carrying the stretcher, get the person in front to hold the handles with their hands behind them so they don't have to walk backwards.
* Once you've finished playing, take the stick handles out of your stretcher so that it can fold up for storing in your medical bag.

7. Time to get rescuing! You'll need two people to carry the stretcher so as not to bump your injured animals too much. Find a teddy that needs your help and carefully place them on the stretcher. Then both of you can take a handle in each hand and lift together and away you go!

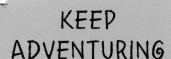

5. Turn your material around and secure the other stick handle on the opposite side in the same way.

6. Flip your stretcher over. You should have two stick handles at each end and the material should hang down a little between the sticks to make a comfy place for your patients to be carried.

KEEP ADVENTURING

Don't forget to use your stretcher in any rescue missions! If you have lots of poorly teddies, why not set up a field hospital? Could you set up beds and treatment stations so everyone gets properly looked after?

MAKE TEDDY MEDICINE

All doctors need some medicine in their medical bags – can you make some pretend medicine to treat your teddy patients?

ADVENTURE KIT

* Water

* Three bowls or containers

* Three types of food colouring

* A pipette or teaspoon

* Some egg cups or small containers

* A plastic syringe

* Teddy patients

WHAT TO DO

1. Put a drop of food colouring into one of the bowls, then fill the container with water and give it a stir so the colour mixes through the water.

2. Do the same with the other two bowls and the other food colours, so that you have three bowls of coloured water.

Remember, this medicine is just for teddies and not for people!

3. Now use your pipette or teaspoon to put a little coloured water into an egg cup. Add a few spoonfuls of another colour and a few drops of the third colour. What colour have you made? What will this type of medicine be for?

HINTS AND TIPS

If you have more types of food colouring, you could make lots of different coloured bowls of water so that you can create an even bigger variety of medicines. Then you'll be able to treat any ailment that comes your way!

4. Grab your teddies and see what they need. They might need a cure for droopy whiskers, a tired tail or an itchy ear. What will you mix up for them?

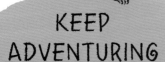

KEEP ADVENTURING

Why not find a bottle to put your mixture in for your teddies to take away with them. You could even make a label for the bottle to remind them what the medicine is for and how often they should take a dose.

5. Use your plastic syringe and draw up a little of the medicine from your egg cup. Sit your teddy down comfortably and gently give him or her a few drops at a time. Perhaps the medicine tastes yucky and your teddy will need a nice cuddle after taking it! Will your teddies be really brave, or will they cry and make a fuss?

TEDDY OINTMENT

Princess Pearl often has to prescribe special cream to help animals feel better. Can you mix up an ointment for any poorly teddies that come your way?

Always ask an adult to help when using scissors

ADVENTURE KIT

* Some conditioner or liquid soap that your grown-up is happy for you to use

* Grass, petals, leaves, or moss

* Safety scissors

* Some small containers

* A spoon

* Some poorly teddies

WHAT TO DO

1. Use your safety scissors to cut your leaves, petals or grass into small pieces.

2. Next, take a small container and spoon in a little of the conditioner.

3. Add in a pinch of grass and a few petal pieces and give the whole thing a mix.

Remember, this ointment is for teddies, not humans! Always check with a grown-up that you can use all of the ingredients safely.

6. Once you've worked out whether your teddy has an aching head, a sore paw or a bumped elbow, use your fingers to very gently rub a little of your ointment into the sore spot.

7. Once a teddy has been treated, lay them down in a quiet place and get to work on the next patient.

8. Depending on the injury, you may have to mix up a new ointment each time. Moss and leaves work best to cool bumps and bruises, while petals work wonders for grazes.

4. Now add some moss or anything else you've found and mix until you think the ointment is ready.

5. Decide which teddy patient will be first. Using your best bedside manner, ask the teddy where it hurts.

KEEP ADVENTURING

Some patients might need to stay in bed for a while. Could you make them a *Get Well Soon* card, or ask their friends and family to come and visit them so they don't get bored?

LEAF PLASTERS

When Zog hurts his nose, Princess Pearl gives him a nice sticking plaster to help him feel better. Can you make some plasters for your teddy patients?

ADVENTURE KIT

* A selection of leaves

* Some elastic bands

* Some teddy patients

* A few small sticks

WHAT TO DO

1. Take a look at your teddy patients to see where they might need a plaster. Have they bumped their head, twisted a snout or broken a wing?

2. Once you know what is wrong with your patient, find a good-sized leaf plaster for the sore area. Wrap the leaf carefully around the snout, wing or head and hold it in place with one hand.

3. Now take an elastic band and wrap it round and round the leaf plaster to hold it in place.

4. If your teddy has a broken leg, they may need a stick splint under their plaster. In this case, place a stick under the leaf and then wrap the elastic band around in the same way. You may need to snap the stick to make it just the right size. The stick will help to keep the leg straight and stop it hurting so much, and will also help it heal in the right position.

5. Once your teddy patient is all plastered up, put them somewhere nice and quiet so they can rest and recover.

HINTS AND TIPS

* Be sure to choose your leaves carefully – you don't want any that have spikes or stings!
* If you're out and about, you could try using some long bits of grass to hold your plaster in place.

KEEP ADVENTURING

What other help might your teddies need while they are recovering? Could they use a crutch or a walking stick to help them get about with their injury? Might they need to be driven around in a toy car, a buggy or a wheelbarrow?

FLYING PRACTISE

Zog is good at flying, though not quite so good at landing ...

To be a dragon ambulance, you'll need to practise flying and landing so you don't bump your patients around too much. Why not do some training before you take on any real life rescues!

ADVENTURE KIT

* Your imagination – to create some enormous dragon wings!

WHAT TO DO

1. First, find something to be your launch pad, where you can practise taking off and landing safely. A low log, a big rock or a giant tyre can work well, but just make sure your grown-up gives your launch pad a thumbs up. There should be lots of space around it so you have room to spread your dragon wings and there isn't any banging, crashing or thumping on the way down!

2. Climb carefully up on to your launch pad. Get your grown-up to help you if you need to.

3. Now warm up your arms and get them ready to be your dragon wings. Stretch them out on either side of you, flap them up and down and wiggle your fingers to get them really tingly.

4. Next, try bending your legs up and down so they'll be super springy and able to send you high into the sky.

KEEP ADVENTURING

Once you're an expert flyer, try tying some teddies on your back with a scarf or a jumper. Does it make it trickier to fly and land with a passenger? Can you be sure not to jolt them around too much?

HINTS AND TIPS

* Hold hands with your grown-up the first few times you try taking off. Once you've got the hang of it you can try it all by yourself.
* If you'd rather not try a launch pad, why not use your wings to skyrocket over a ditch or soar over a puddle.

5. Prepare to fly! Bend your knees and do the most enormous jump as you take off. Don't forget to flap your wings!

6. As you come in to land, remember to bend your knees again and hold your wings out wide to keep you nice and steady.

7. Did you wobble on landing like Zog or did you land perfectly gracefully?

8. Climb up to your launch pad and go for another flight. Keep practising until you feel you can win a golden star!

The Smeds and The Smoos

By a loobular lake on a far-off planet
There lived a young Smed, and her name was Janet.
Not far away on a humplety hill,
There lived a young Smoo by the name of Bill.

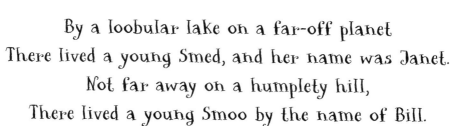

Join Bill and Janet on their out-of-this world adventure as they discover new planets, and explore their own. Practise jumping like Bill, dodge some asteroids, or make your very own colourful aliens…

There's so much to do!

AVOIDING ASTEROIDS

Asteroids are rocks that float around in space.
Try this asteroid game to hone your dodging skills
before your next big space adventure.

ADVENTURE KIT

* A light bouncy ball about the size of a football

* A piece of old material big enough to completely cover your ball

* An elastic band

* A metre-long piece of string

* A ball of string or rope

* Somewhere with plenty of space to tie your asteroid

* Two people to play

WHAT TO DO

1. First, make your asteroid. Lay out your bit of material on the ground and put the ball in the middle. Now gather the four corners of the material and bring them together on top of the ball. Wrap the elastic band around the corners to hold them together. Pull on the four corners so the material sits tightly around the ball. Your ball should now be completely covered with a little tufty tail on the top. This is your flying asteroid.

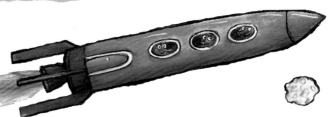

2. Using the ball of string, tie a length about three meters high in an open area. Tie it between trees, or some fence posts.

3. Now tie one end of the metre-long piece of string to your flying asteroid and the other end to the long piece of string tied between trees. Make sure there is lots of space around it. The asteroid should be hanging around tummy height.

KEEP ADVENTURING

What other things can you think of to do with your asteroid? Could you make the string longer and use it to bonk a teddy on the nose or knock down a tower of bricks? Could you tie your asteroid onto a piece of elastic for even more bouncy fun?

HINTS AND TIPS

Make sure the ball you use is soft and light, so it doesn't hurt too much if you do collide with it!

4. Test your asteroid! Can it swing from side to side, can it move in a circle, or even fly up and over the string?

5. Now one person can push the asteroid so it swings from side to side, while the other tries to run past it without being hit. If you get hit, you are out! Take it in turns to be the person swinging and the person running.

6. What other games can you play with the asteroid? Can you swing it to each other and catch it? Can you kick it with your foot or punch it with your fist?

ALIEN ART

Aliens come in all shapes, sizes and colours.
Get colour mixing and see what you can create!

ADVENTURE KIT

* Some old white or cream material –
an old sheet or a tea towel could
work well.

* Safety scissors

* Some water-based colouring pens

* A dish of water

* A pipette or a teaspoon

Always
ask an adult to
help when using
scissors

WHAT TO DO

1. First, lay out your material somewhere nice and flat and use a pen to draw the outline of an alien creature. Keep the shape simple as little fiddly bits will be tricky to cut out.

2. Now use your scissors to cut out your alien outline. Ask a grown-up for help if you need to.

3. Once your outline is all cut out, use the pens to cover it in patches of colour. Dots, lines, squiggles or blocks of colour – you choose!

4. Once you have finished adding colour to your alien, it's time to mix things up! Grab the pipette or a teaspoon and the dish of water. Very carefully, drip a few drops of water on to the edge of your alien outline.

HINTS AND TIPS

Big dots of colour spread really well. Once your material is all wet, stop adding water so that you don't wash all your lovely colour mixtures away.

7. Once your material is soaked in water the colours won't change any more, so leave your alien outline somewhere warm until it's dry and then it's ready to display!

8. Use the rest of your material to cut out more alien shapes and colour them up with your pens and a little water. Can you make a whole family?

5. Sit back and watch as the water spreads through the material.

6. Keep adding drops of water to your material and watch as the colours spread out and mix. Which colours spread the furthest and what happens when two colours meet?

KEEP ADVENTURING

You don't need to stick to designing aliens. Simple shapes and animal outlines look great too. Try putting your colourful creations in the window so the sun shines through them.

BUILD A MINI PLANET

They touched down on Grimbletosh, coated in grime.
They searched Planet Glurch, and found nothing but slime.

What kind of planet would you like to live on?
Why not make one to explore!

ADVENTURE KIT

* Some uncooked cous-cous or rice

* Some poster paint, whatever colour you'd like

* A bowl that can get painty

* A spoon

* A tray that can get painty

* Rocks, leaves, pinecones, sticks and other natural materials

* Some tiny toys to live on your planet

WHAT TO DO

1. First, pour the cous-cous into your tray so you know how much to use. You want there to be enough to generously cover the bottom of the tray and some extra to build mountains and hills.

2. Now dye the cous-cous an exciting space colour. Tip the cous-cous into the bowl and add a good squeeze of paint. Mix the two together with the spoon until the cous-cous is well covered.

3. Tip the cous-cous back into the tray and use the spoon to spread it out. Leave this somewhere warm to dry for a few hours.

4. Once your cous-cous is dry, you are ready to build your planet. Use your fingers to help form the landscape of your planet. Push some cous-cous together to build a mountain or dig right down to make a deep planet crater.

HINTS AND TIPS
* Your cous-cous doesn't need to be one colour – you can make it any colour of the rainbow!
* If you have other dried grains or beans why not use them on your planet as well. Will they be space sand or alien eggs?

KEEP ADVENTURING

Can you build a spaceship to land on your planet? Practise blasting off and landing but take care not to squash any of your planet's creatures!

5. Once your planet surface has started to take shape, you can grab your natural materials and add some features to the landscape. Why not put in some big space rocks, some exciting alien plants and maybe even some extra-terrestrial trees.

6. Now introduce your toys to their new home. Where will they sleep? What will they eat? Will they explore and build houses or will they dig through the planet surface to discover space treasure? Have fun playing!

MAKE A RAINBOW

Janet is red and Bill is blue and their little baby Smoo-Smed is purple. How many colours can you create?

ADVENTURE KIT

* Half a red cabbage

* A big saucepan

* A kettle of hot water

* A grown-up to help you

* A bucket or bowl

* A couple of pipettes or teaspoons

* Some small containers

* Some white vinegar

* Some bicarbonate of soda

Hot water must be handled by a grown-up, so ask your adult to help for this activity.

WHAT TO DO

1. First, ask a grown-up to make your cabbage water by placing the leaves of the red cabbage into the pan and covering them with boiling water from the kettle. Leave the leaves to soak for about 20 minutes or until the water is cool and then your grown-up can fish them out and pop them in the compost. The water you are left with should be a deep purple colour.

2. Pour the cooled purple cabbage water into the bucket or bowl and take it outside to play.

Janet

Bill

HINTS AND TIPS

* White or pale containers work best so you can really see the colours you have made.
* Can you add other things to your cabbage water to see what happens? Do any of the natural things you can find in your park or garden make the cabbage water change colour?

6. Now you know the magic of your ingredients, keep adding different amounts to your cabbage water and see how many colours you can make!

7. Can you make a rainbow? What mixture makes the colour closest to Bill, Janet and to their little Smoo-Smed?

So, what's happening?

Well, the purple cabbage water is known as an indicator solution. If you add an acid like vinegar, the liquid turns pink, and if you add an alkaline substance like bicarbonate of soda, it turns blue.

Baby Smoo-Smed

3. Use your pipette or a teaspoon to fill one of your small containers with the purple cabbage water.

4. Now use a clean pipette to add a few drops of vinegar to the container. What do you notice?

5. Fill another container with cabbage water and this time use the handle of your teaspoon to add some bicarbonate of soda. What happens now?

KEEP ADVENTURING

When you've finished creating colours and making rainbows, pour some vinegar mixture into some bicarbonate of soda mixture for a colourful explosion!

ALIEN OUTLINES

The Smeds and the Smoos meet all sorts of unusual creatures while searching for Bill and Janet. Can you create an amazing new alien species?

ADVENTURE KIT

* A big flattish space where you can lie on the ground

* Someone to lie on the ground and someone to build the outline

* A collection of things you can use to make that outline – try pinecones, conkers, sticks, leaves, toys or building blocks!

WHAT TO DO

1. Start off by deciding who will lie on the ground and who will build the outline.

2. If you are the person lying on the ground, try to make an interesting shape with your body. Put your arms and legs out in a star shape, bend your legs at funny angles or put your hands on your head. Now stay nice and still!

3. If you are the builder, gather the collection of things and start to lay them around the person on the floor. Start with one foot and put the cones or sticks close to their shoes and close to each other. Keep laying cones or sticks all round their legs, body, arms and head.

4. When you've gone all around their outline and have got back to the start you are finished.

5. The person lying on the floor can now stand up carefully and you can both take a look at the outline.

HINTS AND TIPS

* Bigger items make for quicker outline building. Big pinecones will only take a minute or two, tiny stones may take a lot longer!

* Be sure to help the person making the outline get up from the floor once it's done, so they don't knock all the objects out of place.

KEEP ADVENTURING

How many differently shaped outlines can you make with your body? Can you use your collection to write a message on the ground? Why not try leaving your alien land art picture for a new friend to find!

6. Use the rest of your collection to change the outline a little and make it look like a creature from another planet. Can you add antennae? Another arm or a second head? Might this creature have spikes on their feet or flowers on their fingers?

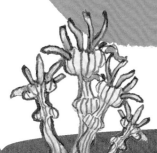

JUMPING

There was joy, jam and jumping.

Can you jump about like a Smoo? Jumping makes us all joyful, is great fun and is good for you too! Really, what better way is there to get around?! Here are some excellent jumping games to try.

ADVENTURE KIT

* Some space for jumping, and some things to jump over or off.

WHAT TO DO

⟡ Set up a jumping course with a row of sticks or logs. Challenge yourself to jump over them all and see how fast you can do it.

☾ Go for a jumping walk and see how many things you can find to jump over: puddles and streams, mole-hills and tufts of grass – endless jumping fun!

☀ Make a jumping circle, where you jump from one thing to another without touching the ground – can you get all the way round?

Before you leap, always remember to have a little check to be sure there is nothing spiky, sharp or living for you to land on!

✈ Jump off low logs, rocks and hillsides – can you make a shape in the air, clap your hands or shout your name before you hit the ground?

☾ Can you jump over your teddies? How many do you dare to jump? Make sure to use squashy teddies so they don't hurt your feet if you accidently land on them.

☛ Try the long jump. Make a mark on the ground to show your jumping off point. Back up, take a good run up and then when you reach the mark, jump as far as you can. Get someone else to mark your landing spot and then the whole family can challenge each other. Who will jump the furthest?!

KEEP ADVENTURING

Jumping games are great for a walk – especially on a cold day. Get your whole family jumping with you!